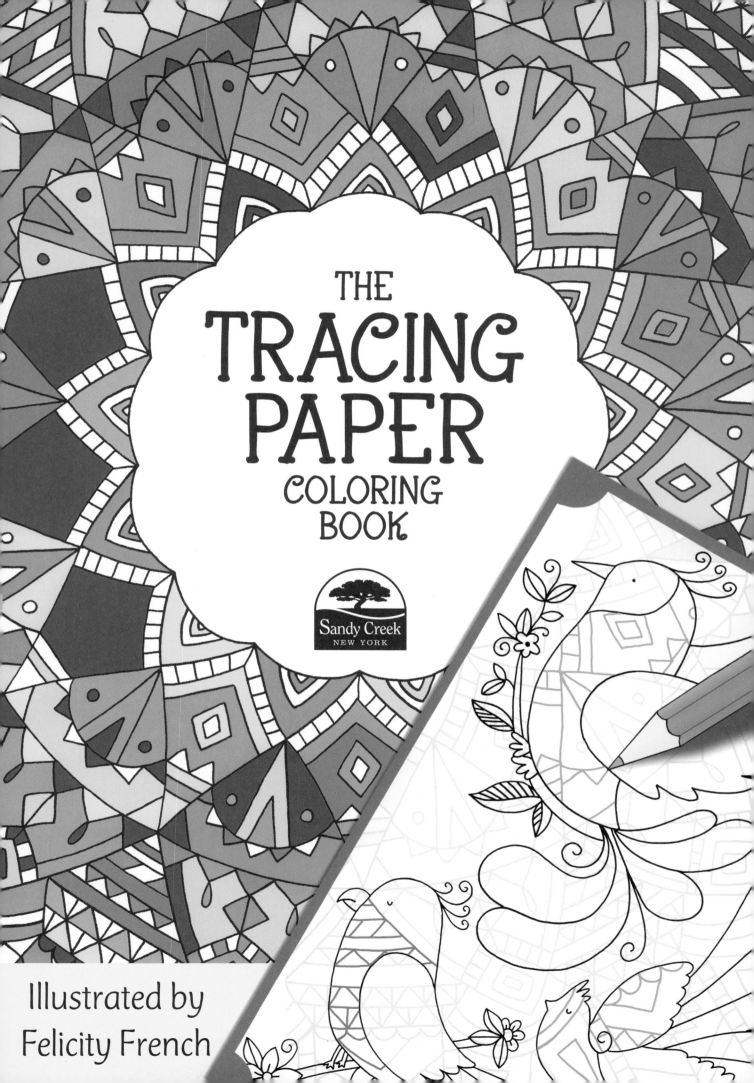

THE TRACING PAPER

COLORING BOOK

Sandy Creek
NEW YORK

Illustrated by

Felicity French

How To Use This Book

This beautiful book is ready for you to color and complete in any way you like.

The pages in this book are filled with pretty patterns and scenes for you to color with pencils or felt-tip pens.

At the front of the book are pages of tracing paper. Some have pictures printed on them for you to complete. Here are some ideas of how to use them:

You could fill the pictures with your own patterns.

You could complete the pictures with bold colors to create stunning stained-glass style pictures that look amazing stuck to a window pane.

Why not tear out a tracing page and trace patterns from one of the pictures in this book?

Some of the tracing paper pages are completely blank for you to design your own pictures. Here are some ideas for how to use them:

Why not choose a picture you like from the book and trace its outline? You could trace in pencil first, and then go over the lines in pen.

You could fill the outline with your own patterns, trace some patterns from the book, or just add bold, beautiful colors.

When using felt-tip pens on tracing paper, let the ink dry for a few minutes to avoid smudges.

Sandy Creek
NEW YORK

An Imprint of Sterling Publishing
1166 Avenue of the Americas
New York, NY 10036

SANDY CREEK and the distinctive Sandy Creek
logo are registered trademarks of Barnes & Noble, Inc.

This 2015 edition published by Sandy Creek.

ISBN: 978-1-4351-6138-2

This book was printed in July 2015 by Ruho Corporation
Sdn. Bhd., 334 Sungai Puyu, 13020 Butterworth,
Penang, Malaysia.

Lot #:
2 4 6 8 1 0 9 7 5 3 1
07/15